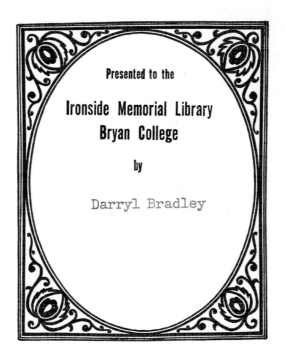

Safed
and
Keturah

BY WILLIAM E. BARTON

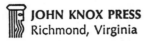

JOHN KNOX PRESS
Richmond, Virginia

STANDARD BOOK NUMBER: 8042-3425-6

LIBRARY OF CONGRESS CATALOG CARD NUMBER: 69-19473

PRINTED IN THE UNITED STATES OF AMERICA

CONTENTS

The Cherry Pie

Two kinds of women are in the world. And besides these two there is Keturah. The one kind maketh a Cherry Pie and taketh out none of the Stones. The other kind taketh out all of the Stones save one.

Now I climbed the Cherry Tree, I and the Robins, and the Robins climbed higher than I, and got at it earlier and stayed at it later, and I was hard put to it to get any of the Cherries. But some of them I gathered, and I brought them in a Basket, and Keturah put the Kettle on, and certain of them she did Can. But some of them she took, and she made thereof a Cherry Pie.

And the Crust thereof was made so that it did melt in my mouth, and the Cherries were rich with their own juice and with Sugar. And there were plenty of them between the Crusts; for after this manner doth Keturah make Cherry Pie.

And in all the Pie there was not one Cherry Stone. And I knew that it would be so, for Keturah made it.

Now there be women who make Cherry Pies for their husbands, and they say unto them, Behold, here is a Cherry Pie with the Stones in; thou hast more time to Pluck them out than I have; and it is lucky for thee that thou get a Cherry Pie, even with the Stones in; and if thou likest it not, thou canst leave it.

And the other kind say, Behold, here is a Cherry Pie, and the Stones thereof have I taken out. But presently her husband biteth hard upon a Stone, and breaketh a Tooth, or crowdeth out a Filling so that it costeth him

Four Dollars to Replace it. And when he chideth his wife, she breaketh into tears, and she saith, Thou art a Cruel Man. For thou givest me no credit for the Stones which I took out, and thou blamest me for the one Stone which I overlooked.

Now the Lord hath mercifully spared me that I married neither of those women, but if I had to choose between them, I would take the woman who removeth no Stones from the Cherries, and biddeth her husband to beware, rather than her who professeth to have removed them all, but who leaveth one Stone to insure his weeping and gnashing of teeth.

And the same is true of life, that men can meet bravely many trials when they have reason to expect them, but he is no friend who promiseth Security when there is one hard Bump that a man must come up against, and be unprepared for it.

But take it from me, when Keturah maketh a Cherry Pie, it is Some Pie.

The Shoes Under the Bed

Of Goodness there be many kinds. For a Shoe becometh good to wear when it becometh bad to look at. Wherefore do I complain when Keturah giveth away any of mine Old Shoes. And Keturah hath provided a place in the Closet, where they may stand in an Orderly Row; but it is my custom when I remove them at night to set them under the edge of the Bed. And at first there is one pair, and then there are other pairs, yea, and a pair of slippers also. And when I arise in the morning, I reach down with mine hand, and take up a Shoe, and if it be not the one that I would wear I set it back and find another.

Now with this System Keturah is not well pleased. Wherefore from time to time doth she gather them up, and set them in array in the Closet. And she saith unto me, Wherefore doth my lord place his shoes under the Bed, which is not Expedient neither Orderly, when he might better place them in a Nice Straight Row in the Closet?

And I said unto her, Thou wast not made as I was made out of the dust of the earth. Thirty and three years ago did God cause a deep sleep to fall upon me. Then took He one of my Ribs and made thee. And thou camest into my life and next to mine heart, not as something from the world without, but as that which already belonged to me, and must be mine so long as the heavens endure. Nevertheless, of all my Ribs art thou the most Unquiet.

And she said, I do admonish thee for thy good.

And I said, O thou fairest among women, were God to establish a school for Husbands, he would make thee Principal. Yea, and I am favored above all men in having become the First and only Graduate of that school, *Magna Cum Laude*.

And Keturah said, Thou hast learned many things, and in much thou hast done well. Yea, and I have yielded the Dipping of the Doughnut in the coffee; why wilt thou not pick up thy shoes?

And I said, If I must, then I needs must.

And I said, Thou hast an Hamper for soiled Clothing,

and a Laundry Bag. I will put my Linen in the Laundry
Bag, if thou wilt allow me a Little Latitude in the matter
of the Shoes.

And Keturah said, For thee that will be doing very
well.

And I answered and said, This will I do, even as I
have promised, but, O Keturah, I do not want to be
Reformed any more than I am already Reformed.

And Keturah said, I verily believe that there are
worse husbands, even than thou.

And then did she kiss me, which is a way that she
hath.

The System of Keturah

We sat at a feast, both I and Keturah, and certain
others. And the Hostess had prepared a Dinner that was
Some Dinner. And we ate thereof and rejoiced. For I
enjoy the eating of such Good Things as God hath given
to men, and I can eat anything save it be Health Foods.

And the Hostess talked of the Duty of Women to
Organize and get their Rights. And she spake right well.
And her husband spake not at all.

And the servants brought in the Good Stuff which
cometh toward the end of the Meal, and Keturah took
thereof, even of the Ice Cream and of the Cakes. But
of the Ice Cream she ate but one small spoonful, and
of the cakes brake she off save it were only a Crumb
from Each Kind, that she might judge how many Eggs
the Recipe called for, and whether they had used Butter
or a Substitute.

But as for me, I cared for none of these things, but ate all that was set before me. For I enjoy all manner of sweet things, even Pies and Cakes, and Ice Cream and Conserves, and Apple Pie, and Mince Pie, and Custard Pie, and Cherry Pie whereof all the Stones have been taken out, and Pound Cake, and Sponge Cake, and Cocoanut Cake, and Chocolate Cake, and Angel Cake, and Wedding Cake, and Fruit Cake, and Sherbets and Preserves, and Strawberry Jam, and Apple Butter and Preserved Figs, and many other kinds. But Keturah careth little for them; nevertheless she taketh them when I sit nigh unto her.

Now while the Hostess was talking about women Organizing and Having a System, Keturah slipped her Full Plate over to me, and I slipped my empty one back to her, and I ate her Ice Cream, and her Cakes besides mine own. And the Hostess saw it not, neither they that sat at meat.

And this hath Keturah done many times in the years wherein we have been married, and her System worketh to her Complete Satisfaction, yea and to mine.

Now on the next day there came to me a man who said, Behold, I have owed thee Fifty Shekels of long time, and thou didst lend this to me when I was Hard Up. Now will I repay thee.

And I embraced him and I thanked him much; for if all men who have borrowed from me would repay me, I should have more wealth than I now possess.

Now it came to pass that night as we sat at meat that I slipped the Plate of Keturah where mine had been, and mine where hers had been. And she looked, and behold, on the plate which I slipped across to her there

were five pieces of gold, each of the value of Ten
Shekels.

And she cried out and said, What is this, and whence
came it?

And I said, Get thee to the sellers of Silk in the
City, and to them that prepare Fine Raiment for women,
and buy thee a Stunning New Frock, and see to it thou
bring me back No Change.

And she asked me saying, Dost thou not need this
Money for other things?

And I said, O thou to the arch of whose eyebrow
the New Moon is a Servant Maid, some women have a
System different from thine, but thine Suiteth me Mighty
Well, and from time to time there shall be Reciprocity.
I also will work thy system and see how well it worketh
in Reverse Gear.

And I thought of men whose Religion consisteth in
Teasing God for what they think are their Rights or
their Desires, and others who delight in giving to God
the best that they have. And I said in mine heart that
those Christians get most out of the Goodness of God
who follow the system of Keturah. For it is a system that
worketh well both with man and God.

The Spliced String

There came to me a man who had made no great
success of his own affairs, but who was eloquent as to
methods whereby other men might Win Success. And
his great god whereby he swore was named Efficiency.

And he spake unto me, saying, The trouble with the Churches, and with the Whole Shooting Match of thy kind of work, is that it knoweth nothing of Efficiency.

And I answered and said unto him,

The home of my boyhood had in it no Fireplace, but we bought our String by the Ball. And the home of my Grandsire had a Vast Fireplace, but they bought no String, for they kept the twine that came wrapped around packages from the store. Wherefore in mine own home if I desired a String, I went to the ball, and cut off how much soever I would. But in the house of my Grandsire if I asked for String, my Grandmother did give me a little piece that had come to her with the Sugar or the Starch. Now there was a day when I was in the house of my Grandsire, and I desired a long String. And I besought my Grandmother, and she gave me Many Short Strings. And I began to tie them together, and to lay out the long string that I was making on the Floor, that I might discern how long it was. And I began at the end of the room that was next unto the Fireplace. And when I had laid down my first string, and tied another to the end of it, I stopped to untangle another string.

Then did a Spark fly out from the Fireplace and light the end of my string. And I knew it not. But I went to the end of the room, and I passed through the door into the next Room, and I tied on more string. And behold, the fire followed me as fast as I tied, and when I looked around, I had but one string, and that was shorter than any one of those that I had tied together. Even so is it with thine Efficiency. He is a god with feet of clay that cannot bear up his own weight, and he burneth up practical results faster than he tieth on his new methods.

And the man said, Thou dost not understand. Be silent and I will explain to thee the workings of Efficiency.

And I said, The greater part of thine efficiency is like unto a Steamboat with a Small Boiler and a Big Whistle. Whenever it bloweth the Whistle the Engine stoppeth, and it bloweth the Whistle continually.

And he saw that I was Hopeless, and he left me.

Of Knowing Too Little and Too Much

There came to the City wherein I dwell a man who delivered a Lecture, and I and Keturah we went. And the subject whereof he spake was one about which he knew very little. But he spread that little over the surface of an Interesting Talk, and the people enjoyed it, and so did we. Yea, and we were profited thereby, although the Lecturer knew little more than he told us.

And there came another man who spake on the same subject, and we went to hear him. And he was a man of Great Erudition. And I said, Now shall we hear something Worth While.

But he began by telling us the History of the Subject and the Various Attempts to Elucidate it. And then he spake of the Various Theories that had been Suggested concerning it, and the books that had been written in Divers Tongues with regard to it. And he said that a certain opinion had been held by men of learning, but was now no longer highly regarded, but that the opinion that was to take its place was in dispute. And he suggested Various Aspects of the theme which he said he could not Discuss because it would require a Volume on any one of them.

And about that time it was time to stop, and he stopped.

And as we journeyed toward our home, Keturah said, He certainly is a man of large knowledge.

And I answered, Yea, and for the purposes of that audience it were better if he had known the tenth part of what he knoweth. For the first man carried all his goods in his show-window, and this man blocked the sidewalk with dray-loads of unopened cases and bales of unassimilable and useless wisdom.

And Keturah said, I have heard that a Little Knowledge is a Dangerous thing.

And I said, Believe it not. A little knowledge is good for seed, but there is such a thing as that a man getteth drowned in his own knowledge. For the first man knew little, but used that little effectively, and the second man knew much, and it was useless.

And I said unto Keturah, Like unto a Spider that is entangled in its own web, so is the man of much knowledge who is unable to employ it. Better is it that a man know little and be able to use it wisely, than to know much and to get lost in the swamp of it.

And Keturah said, Nevertheless, I think that knowledge is good, and much knowledge is better than little.

And I said, All human knowledge is small, and the difference between the man who knoweth much and the man who knoweth little is too small to waste much time in futile distinctions. For in the sight of God the wisdom of both is foolishness. But the value of knowledge is in the use of it.

And Keturah inquired of me, saying, Art thou a man of much knowledge or of little?

And I answered, If so be that I am able to use my knowledge and get away with it, what doth it matter if it be little or large? Behold, though I be ignorant, yet have I no trouble in finding people yet more ignorant, and if the stream wherein they swim is over their head, what doth it matter if it be an inch or ten thousand cubits?

And Keturah said, I do verily believe that among the ignorant men of earth there be some who are more ignorant than my lord; and if any of them do think thee wise, I shall not tell them that it is not so.

The Stone Halfway Up

There came unto me one of the great men in Israel, upon whom God had laid the burden of a Great Task. And he said unto me, Safed, art thou ever Weary?

And I answered him, saying, Well, hardly ever.

And he inquired of me again, saying, Art thou ever Completely Discouraged?

And I answered him, I have ever one more String to my Bow.

And he said, I am Completely Tired Out; and what is worse, I am Discouraged.

And I said unto him, O my friend, God hath highly

honored thee in giving to thee a Task beyond thy Strength. Listen to the word of a wise man, who thus spake unto me, Seek not for tasks to which thy strength is equal; seek rather for strength adequate to thy tasks.

And he said, Yea, but this is Up-Hill all the way.

And I said, There is no Hill that reacheth to the sky, and every Hill hath beyond its Summit a Down-Hill Side. If thou stop now, halfway up, thy task shall roll back upon thee and crush thee; but if thou put a little more Punch into thine Up-Hill Rolling of the Stone, then shalt thou come to the Crest, and the thing will roll more easily downward.

And he said, I know that it is so, but I fear that this task will kill me.

And I laughed him to scorn, and I said, Take courage; for thou shalt yet dance upon the Coffin-lid of this job.

And as he rose to go, I said unto him, Listen, O my friend, and mark well my words. Some men when they die will be Dust; but by the grace of God it shall not be so with me nor yet with thee. We shall not be Dust, but Ashes.

The Millionaire and the Scrublady

There is a certain Millionaire, who hath his Offices on the Second Floor of the First National Bank Building. And when he goeth up to his Offices he rideth in the Elevator, but when he goeth down, then he walketh.

And he is an Haughty Man, who once was poor,

and hath risen in the World, and he is Self-made Man
who worshipeth his maker.

And he payeth his Rent regularly on the first day of
the month, and he considereth not that there are Human
Beings who run the Elevators, and who Clean the Windows, hanging at a great height above the Sidewalk,
and who shovel Coal into the furnaces under the Boilers.
Neither doth he at Christmas time remember any of
them with a Tip or a Turkey.

And there is in that Building a Poor Woman who
Scrubbeth the Stairs and the Halls. And he hath walked
past her often but hath never seen her until Recently.
For his head was high in the air, and he was thinking
of More Millions.

Now it came to pass on a day that he left his
Office, and started to walk down the Stairs.

And the Scrublady was halfway down; for she had
begun at the top, and was giving the stairs their First
Onceover. And upon the topmost Stair, in a wet and
soapy spot, there was a Large Cake of Yellow Soap.
And the Millionaire stepped upon it.

Now the foot which he set upon the Soap flew
eastward toward the Sunrise, and the other foot started
on an expedition of its own toward the going down of
the Sun. And the Millionaire sat down upon the Topmost Step, but he did not remain there. As it had been
his Intention to Descend, so he Descended, but not in
the manner of his Original Design. For he descended
faster, and he struck each step with a sound as it had
been of a Drum.

And the Scrublady stood aside courteously, and let
him go. And he stayed not on the order of his going.

And at the bottom he arose, and considered whether he should rush into the Office of the Building and demand that the Scrublady be fired; but he considered that if he should tell the reason there would be great Mirth among the occupants of the Building. And so he held his peace.

But since that day he taketh notice of the Scrublady, and passeth her with Circumspection.

For there is no man so high or mighty that he can afford to ignore any of his fellow human beings. For a very Humble Scrublady and a very common bar of Yellow Soap can take the mind of a Great Man off his Business Troubles with surprising rapidity.

Wherefore, consider these things, and count not thyself too high above even the humblest of the children of God.

Lest haply thou come down from thy place of pride and walk off with thy bruises aching a little more by reason of thy suspicion that the Scrublady is Smiling into her Suds, and facing the day's work the more cheerfully by reason of the fun thou hast afforded her.

For these are solemn days, and he that bringeth a smile to the face of a Scrublady hath not lived in vain.

The Long Walk

The daughter of the daughter of Keturah hath a little friend who cometh to see her, and playeth with her in the Yard, hard by the Window, where their voices may be heard inside the House. And mostly they play

very Happily; but now and then for the sake of Variety
they indulge in Argument and Comparison like grown
Folk. And it was upon a day that they got thus into a
Friendly Scrap, the first part of which I heard not. But
the Argument had reached a stage where the daughter
of the daughter of Keturah was advancing and backing
the other little damsel off the Map, and the other little
girl could only answer, I did not, or You can not, or It
is not.

And the daughter of the daughter of Keturah said,
I can walk Fifty-nine miles.

And the other little girl said, You can not.

And the daughter of the daughter of Keturah said,
I can take my Grandpa's hand and keep up with him,
and he can walk Fifty-nine miles, and I can walk Fifty-
nine miles with him if I hold his hand.

And the other little damsel said, You can not.

Then did the daughter of the daughter of Keturah
tell unto the other little girl how great and good a
Grandpa she had. And I am too modest a man to write
down what she said; but if George Washington and
Solomon and a few others were to live in one, peradventure he might be a Second-cousin or a Remote Acquaint-
ance of a man such as the daughter of the daughter of
Keturah described.

And the other little girl was speechless; for she could
not say, Thy Grandpa is not the only Pebble on the
Beach; I also have a Grandpa whose hair is fully as
Gray and whose Bald Spot is larger than thy Grandpa's;
for the daughter of the daughter of Keturah had carried
the matter beyond all comparison. And the other little
girl could only change the subject, and say,

I can kick your whole house down and all your trees.

And the daughter of the daughter of Keturah, knowing that she had won out, said sweetly,

Go ahead.

Now there is no man who knoweth so well as I how far from right is the estimate of the little maiden concerning the goodness and the greatness of her Grandpa. Nevertheless it pleased me more than any man can understand who is not a Grandpa; for unto none others hath the Lord given wisdom to know of such matters. And the next time a man goeth by and bloweth a small whistle, she shall have a Red Balloon.

For apart from her beautiful delusion concerning the poor man concerning whom I pray my God that she may be never undeceived, the little maiden is not wholly wrong. For when she holdeth my hand she can do things which otherwise she could not do.

And I prayed unto my God a prayer, and I said,

O my God, Thou hast permitted us through the gift of little lives such as these to discern spiritual truths which Thou hast hid from the wise and prudent and revealed unto babes, that so we might enter into the Kingdom of Heaven as little children. Grant unto me this, O my Father, that I shall hold so fast to Thine Hand that the journey that would otherwise be impossible shall be possible for me, and the task that would have been too great may be accomplished through Thy strength. For I can do all things through Him that strengtheneth me, and if I hold Thy Hand I can run and not be weary, and walk and not faint.

Things That Are Small

I was putting on my Outer Garments, and going unto a Committee Meeting. And I was late. And Keturah said unto me, Go thou by the way of the house of our Daughter, and give unto her this Package, and speak unto her such and such Messages, and then go thou unto thy Committee Meeting.

And I did even as she said unto me. But I was in haste, and I tarried not long, nor sat down.

And as I hastened away, I heard a great Cry, and I turned back to see if the daughter of the daughter of Keturah had broken her Neck. And she had not broken her Neck, but I had broken her Heart.

And I asked, What is the matter with my little girl?

And she sobbed and she answered, Grandpa hardly spoke to me. I am so little he does not care for me.

Now when I heard this I was smitten to mine heart, for it had been even as she said. And the little maiden is unto me as the Apple of mine Eye. But I had been in an Hurry, for there was a Committee Meeting, and I was late.

And I entered the House, and I took her into mine arms, and I sat in a Chair with the little maiden in my lap, and with her Golden Hair upon my Shoulder, and I said, Let the Committee Meeting go hang.

And she said, You do love me, Grandpa, don't you, even if I am small?

And I said, My dear, I love thee as much as if thou wert the Fat Lady in the Side Show, and maybe more. Yea, I do not think it would be possible for a Grandsire to love a little damsel more than I love thee.

And she put her arms around my neck, and the Committee Meeting just had to mosey along as best it could till I got there.

Now after a while she got down, and we bade each other an Happy Good-bye, and I went my way. And as I went, I thought of the children of God who sometimes get to feeling just the same way, and thinking that their Heavenly Father doth not care for them because they are so Little, and He is busy with Great Things.

And I prayed unto my God on behalf of all such Heart-Broken children of His, that He will gather them in His arms, and comfort them, and tell them to cast all their care upon Him, for it Mattereth to Him concerning them.

The Late Arrival

There liveth in a certain city a man whose name is John Smith, and he hath been for many years an Honest and Inconspicuous Citizen. And it came to pass after many years that his name began to appear Among Those Present; and it seemed unto him Mighty Good to get into the outer edges of the Limelight, and he began to yearn for a place a little nearer unto the Center of the Stage.

Now there was a great Public Banquet at the leading Hotel, and all the Prominent Citizens shook their Dress Suits out from the Moth Balls and were present. And John Smith had a place at the Further End of the Speakers' Table.

And after the Hoi Polloi were seated, then did the

Occupants of the Speakers' Table file in and take their seats, while the Band played, It Looketh unto me like a Big Night Tonight. And John Smith felt good clean down into his Boots to think that a Part of that Salute was for him.

Now there was one Vacant Seat at the Speakers' Table, and they all knew whose it was. For G. Fred Jones did habitually arrive late. And when he came in about twelve minutes after all the others were seated, then did the Band play, Hail to the Chief. And the Presiding Officer walked over and said, So good of thee to come; we feared that thou hadst been detained.

Now John Smith believed all this, and he said: I am wise to this little Game. It is he who cometh late that getteth the Glad Hand, whereas he who cometh in with the Bunch is unnoticed.

Now there came another Banquet and John Smith had a seat a little further from the end and a little nearer to the center of the Speakers' Table, and he arrived fifteen minutes late. And he said: Now for the Big Noise when I enter.

And behold, as he drew nigh, he heard the sound of Music, for the Band was playing, Hail, Hail, the Gang's All Here, and he slipped in wholly unobserved.

When he sought for his seat, behold it had been given unto another, for the Presiding Officer said: We thought thou wert out of Town. Now behold, there are some good seats yonder by the Door. Go thou away back and be thou seated.

And he went away back and sat down. And he did not enjoy the Banquet a little bit, neither did his food that he ate that night agree with him, and his applause of the Speeches lacked something of Heartiness.

And he said within himself: Behold, I have several times made of myself a Fool, but this is the worst in all my sweet young life. For I perceive that he who setteth his foot upon the First Round of the Ladder of Publick Recognition is a Fool if he thinketh that he hath already attained. For he who hath arrived can work those little stunts that increase his Popularity, whereas if a man more obscure doth attempt one of them, he only increaseth his obscurity.

And I considered this Truthful Tale, and I said: Little Fishes Should Keep nigh unto the Shore. Nevertheless there is yet hope for John Smith, for he is capable of learning Wisdom from his own Folly, and that is the only real way in which Wise Men such as I have attained Wisdom. For we all started with a Large Endowment of Folly, and it departeth very slowly from even the Wisest of Men.

The Great Game

I journeyed by Boat in the Good Old Summertime; and I put off my Prophet's Mantle, and I wore a Short Coat and a Cap and I looked like a Minister off on his Vacation save that I Draw the Line at a Red Necktie. And the Ship's Clock struck Five Bells, which meaneth Half Past Six. So I went unto the Dining Room, and the Head Steward gave me a place at a Table where Three People already were seated. And one of them was a Lady, and she sat Over Against me.

And she sought to put me at my ease at once, and to make me a Member of the Party. And she Spake unto her Husband, but she looked at me, and she said:

Now this is Very Pleasant to have this Fourth Place filled, for I never like to sit at a Table with a Vacant Place across from me. And I am sure we welcome this Gentleman to our Little Group. And, furthermore, I am persuaded that he is a Good Bridge Player. And after we have Dined we may sit in the Aft Cabin and play a Pleasant Little Game.

And her Husband, being thus admonished to Follow her Lead, addressed me, saying, Welcome to our City.

And we spake of the Weather, and How Much Better it was to travel by Boat than by Rail in Hot Weather, and how it was a Calm Night. And then the Lady resumed the Subject of Bridge. And she said,

Tell me, am I not Right? I know a Good Bridge Player every time. And this also have I observed, that all Really Good Bridge Players deny it.

Now if I had admitted it she would have felt sure she was right, and if I had denied it she would have felt more sure. Therefore, I held my peace, and spake of other things.

But again she asked me, and I said, I play a more serious game.

And she said, Oh, I know! You men all think Poker is so much better than Bridge! But Poker is a Man's Game and I like it not. But I just love Bridge.

And I said, The Apostle Paul speaketh of Epaphroditus that he played the Gambler with his life for the Lord's sake. And he commendeth his associates as Men who had Hazarded their lives for the Kingdom of God. I play the Great Game of Life, face to face with an inscrutable player whose Hand is hidden so that I see not the cards she holdeth. And some men call her

Nature, and some men Fate or Destiny, but the servant of God playeth ever in the darkness with an Angel that will not tell its name. And the hazard is this, that in a world where many of the Cards are black and some are red, I wager my very soul that Hearts are trumps. I play the Game of Life with all that I possess staked on my belief that, though Money driveth men mad, the Diamond and all that it representeth doth not take the trick; that in a world where Cruelty doth abound, and War doth rage, and Death doth walk abroad, the Spade is not the card that winneth all things upon the green table of the earth. I stake mine all upon my faith that Hearts are trumps, and that Love is the highest card in the pack. I bet my life that Love is after all the Greatest thing in the world. That God is love, and men are brothers, and that at the end of the Game when we all Cash In we shall find that he who said that Diamonds were trumps will go where his Money will purchase nothing, and he who hath said that Clubs were trumps will go where clubs and cannon count for nothing, and he who hath said that Spades were trumps will find that Death is not a finality, but Life and Love and God and Duty and Heroism and Sacrifice Win Out. That is the Great Game which I play. And the Stakes are High. I have Bet my Life as Epaphroditus did, and have hazarded my soul like the three men in the Burning Fiery Furnace. I have made my wager that God is good, and that Love is the final law of the universe.

And I ceased, and the Lady said,

Oh, I just *do love* to hear you talk! Oh, I think it's *just grand* to be able to talk like that!

And of Bridge spake they no more.

The Moving Vehicles

I rode in a Railway Train, and it was late at a Junction where I changed Cars. And a man rode with me and changed at the same place. And we got out of one train and into another and were quick about it. And he said unto me, For a man of thine age, thou leavest and boardest a train with agility.

And he asked, What is thine Occupation?

And I answered and said, I am employed in jumping on and off Moving Vehicles, such as Cabs and Taxis and Automobiles and such like.

And he said, In what Race dost thou perform these Stunts?

And I said, The Human Race.

And he said, Thou speakest in Riddles.

And I said, There are two processions that never stop, and they go in opposite ways, and I ride in them both. And I jump constantly from one to the other. For I ride behind the Hearse and have no time to change my clothes or my mind before I ride to the Wedding. And the sounds of the Dirge mingle ever in mine ears with those of the Wedding March. And the rattling of the rice on the windows of the carriage is echoed by the sound of the dust falling upon the coffin in the grave.

And he said, I cannot understand how a man can stand it. I should think it would drive thee crazy. But perchance it cometh not so hard when a man getteth used to it?

And I said, Friend, I never shall get used to it. There lieth some part of my heart in every grave where I have stood and committed dust to dust. The joy of the bride and the hope of the bridegroom are as mine own joy and hope.

And he said, Thine must be a sadly mixed life. I envy thee not thy job. Yea, I have thought mine own job an hard one, but thou canst give me cards and spades.

And I said, O my friend, there again thou art mistaken. For my work is one of joy. When I go unto the house of mourning, there do I go with a message of comfort and hope. And when I meet the bride and the groom before the Altar of God and bless them ere they go forth to the establishment of a new home, then do I add to their joy. And when they come again and meet me there and bring with them a little child, of whose like is the Kingdom of God, then again is their joy the more perfect by reason of that which I say and do in the name of the Lord.

And he said, Nevertheless, I shall remember hereafter that the business of being a prophet of the Lord calleth for more agility than I had supposed.

And I said, There may be no harm in that.

Perhaps

I spake unto Keturah, saying, I must hie me unto the shop of the Barber.

Now the daughter of the daughter of Keturah was there, and she spake unto me, saying, Grandpa, the Barber giveth unto every one that hath his hair cut a Stick of Gum. Wilt thou bring the Gum unto me?

And I answered and said unto her,

Alas, my little maiden, it cannot be. Youth hath many privileges which belong not unto those advanced in years, and among them is the privilege of receiving Gum from the Barber. If there come unto the shop of the Barber a nice little girl, and she sitteth very quietly in his chair while he bobbeth her hair just below her ears, unto her doth he give a Stick of Gum. And if per-adventure there come unto his shop a Small Boy, and he maketh no fuss, but remaineth quietly in the chair, and goeth forth smiling, unto him also doth the Barber give a Stick of Gum. But unto aged men like unto thy Grandpa doth he give no Gum, yea, though they be never so good. Rejoice in thy youth, and congratulate thyself that thou hast entered into the Kingdom of Heaven as a little child. For youth there is balm in Gilead, but for thy Grandpa there is no Gum in Goodness.

And she said, Grandpa, across the street from the shop of the Barber is a Drug Store. And in the Drug Store there is Gum. Howbeit, they give thee not one stick but five, and thou shalt give unto the man in the white coat a Nickel.

And I said, Between one stick which the Barber giveth free and five sticks which the man with the white coat in the Drug Store giveth for a nickel, is a measurable difference in good hard Cash.

And she waited a moment, and she said, Grandpa, wilt thou bring me the Gum?

And I said, Perhaps.

And she considered, and she asked, saying, Grandpa, what is the meaning of "Perhaps"?

And I said, The word Perhaps is a word of widely different connotations. For sometimes it meaneth, Not if I can think of some good reason for not doing it. And again it meaneth, It shall never be done. And once, a very long time ago, when I asked something of thy Grandma, and she said, Perhaps, that was a meaning still different.

And she said, Grandpa, what doth Perhaps mean when a little girl asketh her Grandpa for Gum and she asketh him very nicely and sayeth Please?

And I said, It meaneth that she shall have the Gum.

And she got it.

Now Keturah heard all this, and she said nothing, but I saw her smiling as though the little maiden were learning some things which her grandmother knew a long time ago.

And I said unto Keturah, I wonder if I could write a Parable about the different meanings of a word?

And Keturah said, Perhaps.

The Guest-Room Towels

There came to me a man who said, The trouble with thee, and with the Church, and with all who labor with thee, is that thy Methods are Old. We are living in a New Age, and the Old Methods are Inadequate.

And I answered, Thou speakest truly, and perhaps wisely.

And he said, How is it that if what I say is Certainly True it is only Possibly Wise?

And I answered him, Because there are no kinds of unwisdom so great as those that are founded on Truth that is Ill Considered. What New Methods dost thou advocate?

And he Got Busy with a Line of Talk about his New Methods, that never had been tried anywhere, and which were certain of but one thing, that they never would work.

And he said, How dost thou like my New Methods?

And I said unto him,

I went to a certain city, and lodged with a friend who sent me to my bed in the Guest Chamber. And it was a Comfortable Chamber, and his wife had made it ready for my coming. And among the other Preparations, she had hung the towel-rack full of New Linen Towels, which she had purchased by the Dozen, and there were Six of them in my Room. And they were Very Nice Towels, and well worth the Price that she paid, for Linen was Going Up. But when I essayed to wipe my face upon them, I could not do it. For those Towels were every one of them as Stiff and as Shiny as a Sheet of Tin, and likewise as Impervious to Water. So I mussed them up, one of them and yet another and another till I had polished my face with the Metallic Surface of all six of them.

And I said unto him, There must needs be New Methods, and I would not be last in the use of any of them that are good. Neither do I care to be the first to dry my face upon a New Towel. Let him that is ambitious for New Experiments try it before me, and after it hath gone to the Laundry and come back, less Shiny but more Serviceable, then will I try it. It is enough for me that I must wear my own New Boots.

The Courage of the Captain

It came to pass many years ago, that I journeyed, and I rode upon a Steamboat upon the Great River, even the Mississippi. And there occurred a fight upon the lower deck of the boat, and one man stabbed another man in the neck, so that he bled much. And he would have stabbed him again and killed him, save that the Captain descended from the Hurricane Deck, and whether he descended by the Stairs or by a Parachute, or whether he Leaped Down, no one could remember. And the Captain came between the men as they fought, and took away the knife from the man who had it, and brought it unto me with the blood still wet upon it, and said, Here is a Pretty Little Souvenir of life upon the River.

And I have that knife unto this day.

Now on that boat they told me much about the Captain, how that he feared God, but neither man nor devil; and how that he was Boss of the Boat from the Boiler Room to the Pilot House, and that no man dared bat an eye until he first had permission from the Old Man. For upon the Mississippi the name of the Captain of all boats is the Old Man.

And the Captain took me into his own room hard by the Pilot House, and behold, it was a Young Arsenal. For he had a Magazine Rifle, and a Pair of Revolvers, and some more Revolvers, and a Knife. And men spake softly when they passed that room, for few of them had seen the inside of it, and they had heard terrible things about the number of men whom the Captain had slaughtered and eaten before breakfast when they got Rambunctious on his boat.

But all men held the Old Man in honor, neither was there a man on the boat but would have fought for him, save that the Old Man bade every man stand back and not get hurt while he attended to matters.

And when the Captain fought, he carried with him no Gun nor Knife nor Stick, but his Bare Hands only. And in his room were Dirks and Guns and Brass Knuckles that he had taken away from men who fought.

Now after many years I met the Captain, and he had retired from the River. And we sat and talked long together.

And I said, I have seen many brave men, but I incline to the Opinion that thou art a Little Bit the bravest piece of sheer manhood I have ever known.

And the Captain said, Deceive not thyself. I am a man of Great Timidity. Therefore did I always make it a point to get into the Fight Right Away; and when I got in, then, of course, even a coward doth know that he must see it through. But had I waited to consider, then should I never have fought; for I am Very Timid. But it was my Duty to keep Order on my Boat, and when I dealt with Gamblers and Cutthroats and with drunken Roustabouts, then did I know exactly what I was Up Against, and acted accordingly.

And I asked him, How many men hast thou killed and eaten?

And he said, It is my daily comfort and for it I devoutly thank my God, that I never inflicted any permanent injury on any fellow man.

And I said, How often didst thou get hurt?

And he said, I was on the River from the time I was eight years old until I was three score and ten, and I never got a scratch.

And I said, I still think thee a most brave man.

But he answered, Nay, it was lucky for me that men knew not how much of a Coward I was, and that I never had time to think. For being a Timid Man, I got into the fight at the start.

And I said, Blessed are the peacemakers who get into the fight at the start, and save lives and do brave deeds and keep the boat in order and neither hurt nor get hurt.

And he said, It may be so. But I was always a Timid Man.

But I still think him the Bravest Man I have known.

Rising Above the Clouds

I rode upon a Railway Train; and we were in the Rocky Mountains. And we awoke in the morning, and the Train was climbing, with two Engines pulling us, and one pushing behind. And we were nigh unto Twelve Furlongs above the Sea.

And it came to pass as we ascended, that there were Clouds below us, and Clouds upon the sides of Mountains, but there were no Clouds above us, but the clear shining of the Morning Sun.

And there came unto me a small Girl and her younger Brother, who were riding upon the Train, and we talked

about the Clouds. For so did John Ruskin and Aristoph-
anes, and the little lad was very happy, and he said,

I have never been above the Clouds before.

And his sister was Worldly-wise. And she said, A
Cloud ain't nothing but just fog.

And he said, Nay, but this is more. And behold now,
how then is a Cloud just under us, and we ride upon
the top of it?

And she said, We are on the Rails, just as we always
have been; and there can't nobody ride on a Cloud.

And the boy said, Jesus can ride upon a Cloud;
for I saw a Picture of Him.

And the little girl said, Yes, but that ain't us.

Now the little girl may have been right; but I thought
within myself that this world hath too many people who
look out on Life through her windows. For they see no
sunlit Clouds, but only Fog; and they have little faith
in rising above Clouds, but have confidence only in the
Rails.

And I do not despise Rails, nor advise people to
discard them and ride upon Clouds. Nevertheless, I have
seen people rise above Clouds, and live in the sunlight
of God. And I have known others who, whenever it is
said unto them, Thus have other men done, or thus did
the good Lord Jesus, make reply, Yes, but that ain't us.

And if it is spoken concerning the House of God,
Thus did the Synagogue in Jonesville, and thus was
it done by the Church in Smithville, they answer, Yes,
but that ain't us.

And if it be said, Thou shouldest be a better man,
for other men have risen above thy Clouds and thine
Infirmities, they say, Yes, but that ain't us.

And when it is said, Thus hath the grace of God abounded in other lives, they say, Yes, but that ain't us.

But if it ain't, why ain't it?

For this cause did God dwell in human flesh, that men should never count any good thing impossible that they behold in the dear Lord Jesus.

For He is our peace, who hath broken down all middle walls, that men should no longer say, But that ain't us.

The Oyster Shell

I have a friend who hath a Summer Cottage by the Seaside. And he said unto me, Come and spend a day with me and I will give thee the Time of thy Sweet Young Life. And I spent the day, and he did all that he said he would do, and among the things that he did to me was a Shore Dinner. And we ate Clam Chowder and Fried Mackerel, and Stewed Cod and Baked Blue-fish, and Lobster Salad. Likewise did we eat Stewed Clams and Oysters on the Half Shell. And I gave thanks to God who made me to suck of the Abundance of the Seas and of treasures hid in the Sands.

Now while we were eating the Oysters I was thinking, and I said, He was a Brave Man who ate the first Oyster. And as I spake I bit upon something hard. And behold it was a pearl, albeit not a very good one.

And we spake of the Pearl, and how it cometh of an Hurt to the Oyster, that is made by a Grain of Sand, that getteth into the Shell, and the Oyster cannot get it out; and how it Woundeth him sore, so that there cometh from the Oyster a very precious Juice that congealeth where the Sand doth irritate, and maketh a pearl.

And my friend saith, It is a pity that Pearl thou hast found is not a good one; for then couldest thou have sold it and gotten thee gain.

And I answered, Though I sell it not, yet have I gotten gain therefrom.

And he said, Tell me how.

And I said, The Oyster is not in all respects the highest type of a Christian; yet in this hath he something to teach even to Christian men, so that there is no man but may learn from him and be wiser.

And he said, It may be so, but all this is news to me.

And I said, Oh, my friend, the race of mankind liveth each man in his own Oyster Shell, and no man knoweth fully what hurt another man hideth. But there is no shell that shutteth out the irritating Sands of Grief and Circumstance, and few men meet the cutting, wounding intrusions of life so well as doth the Oyster. I have been young and am now old, and I have seen men in all manner of misfortune, and have seen them meet life's adversities in every possible manner. There may not be much that a Christian can learn from an Oyster, but the Good God so made the world as that even the Oyster may speak to men who now are crushed by their sorrows and say to them, Heal thy hurt with a Pearl.

The Barometer

There was a day when I went down to the Sea in Ships, and made a Voyage on Great Waters. And when I returned to my Home, I brought a Barometer, which Sailors call a Glass. And Keturah esteemeth it not, and declareth that it telleth what the Weather was Yesterday. But I think Highly of it.

Now there came to me a man who had been a Sinner, and he had Repented. But at times his Temptations beset him so that he Fell. And he wept much as he told me of his sins.

And I said, How often didst thou Get Drunk in the old days?

And he answered, Just once, and it Lasted Over Continually.

And I said, When thou didst first repent, how frequently didst thou fall?

And he said, About once in a Month.

And I said, How long is it now Between Falls?

And he said, Sometimes Three Months, and Sometimes Six. I gain a Little, but it is Very Slow. And the longer it is between Falls, the more I Despise Myself that I should fall at all.

And I asked him, What dost thou think of the Weather?

And he was astonished at my question, but he answered and said, It is a Rainy Day.

And I said, This is a fine Barometer. What doth it say?

And he saith, The Finger pointeth to Rain.

And I tapped lightly on the Glass and the finger moved upward a Very Little.

And I said, Before tomorrow Night it will be Fair.

And he said, How can that be when the Barometer saith Rain?

And I said, There was an old Sailor man who swore to me by the gods of the sea, even Neptune and Davy Jones, saying, A Barometer is an Everlasting Liar if thou readest only the words around the Dial. For it is not a Question of Where it Pointeth only, but Which Way it Moveth.

And I said, My friend, thy Soul's Barometer Moveth Upward. Trust God, keep up thy Courage and thou shalt Surely Conquer.

And as he went his way, Lo, the clouds parted, and there appeared a Little Patch of Blue Sky.

The Cocoanut Cakes

I was not always aged, but was once young. And I sojourned in a School of the Prophets. And on the day before the Sabbath I rode every week Nineteen Miles that on the Sabbath Day I might speak the word of God to the people in a Little White Synagogue with a Tall Steeple. And on the day after the Sabbath I rode back again. And there were times when the Roads were bad, so that for every foot that my horse went forward, he sank in the mud unto the depth of an half of a foot; so I went down through Nine Miles and the half of a Mile of mud before I got there. But when

I arrived then did the good people welcome me into warm homes and clean beds and set before me hot suppers.

For I boarded around among them.

And at the first place where I abode for a Sabbath, the good woman set before me Cocoanut Cake. And I ate plentifully thereof.

Now the women of the other homes inquired of her, saying, How didst thou like the Young Minister? And is he hard to entertain? And doth he cause thee much trouble? And is he fussy? And what doth he like to eat?

And she said, He is not fussy, and he keepeth out of the kitchen, and when he hath a book he doth not bother the hostess with Theology; and he said unto me that Cocoanut Cake is his Favorite Cake.

Now all the women told all the other women, saying, The Young Minister loveth Cocoanut Cake.

And they all knew how to make Cocoanut Cake, and they all made it. And wherever I went, there did they set before me Cocoanut Cake.

Now thou wilt surely think within thine heart that I got so much Cocoanut Cake that I abhorred it, and that I have never liked it since. But thou hast another Think coming. For thou knowest not what sort of Cocoanut Cake the women of that Parish make. Yea, for three years did I eat it with scarce ever a break in the record, save that there also they make Cake with Maple Sugar Frosting. And he that hath eaten that kind of Cake knoweth that that is about the best ever.

For there be some things of which no man can ever have too much. And when mine heart goeth back across the years, then do I remember the long rides, and the times that I drave up in the dark and the cold, and how they stabled mine horse knee-deep in clean straw, and put a sack of oats under the buggy seat when I departed, and maybe also a Bushel of Potatoes or a Sack of Apples or a Can of Maple Syrup. And I know that I shall never have too much of any of the good things which they bestowed upon me, nor of the love that was in them all.

And now and then as the years go by, and one and another of those I loved is called unto his long home, then do they send for me to come and say a word of love before the dust returneth unto dust. And ever there is some good woman who hath a table set for me in her home; and there do I always find Cocoanut Cake.

And whenever I eat of Cocoanut Cake that is Unusually Nice, then do I remember the friends of my early Ministry as a Messenger of God, and I love them yet.

Profanity

They laid a water-pipe in the road at the place where I and Keturah go in Summer; and the soil was stubborn and rocky. And when the men came for to dig, I took a Spade and digged for a little time in the trench with them. Likewise did I with the Pick and the Crowbar.

And the men said, Thou canst do work such as we do save it be only in one thing. For if we strike more Rock than we expect, or if the water flow into our trench, or if peradventure it cave in so that we have to dig it out again, canst thou do thy part of the Swearing?

And I answered and said, I will do it all.

And they said, It is liable to be a Large Contract.

And I said, Even so, I will assume it. All the Swearing that this job requireth, leave it to me.

And when the ditch caved in, or the water stood in the trench so that they had to pump it out, or they struck rock and had to blast, then did they say one to another, Swear not: for that is Safed's job.

And thus it came to pass that no Swearing was necessary, but only Muscle and Pumps and some Dynamite.

Now I considered how many people there be who swear by the use of Profane words, or by the Slamming of Doors, or by Scolding, and I thought that it would be well if there might be appointed an Official Swearer for all such like occasions, and that he should consider the matter carefully before Swearing or Scolding and see if some other way would answer just as well. For if the digger strike rock, and must use Dynamite as well as swear, he might as well use Dynamite instead of Swearing. And if Kindness will do the work instead of Scolding, then is the Scolding wasted or maybe worse.

Therefore am I open to Employment wherever there is need, to take the responsibility of all the Swearing and all the Scolding that shall be required, and if it be left to me, there will not be much of either.

For one should neither Swear nor Scold if there be any other way to accomplish the result desired; nor unless it is sure that Swearing or Scolding will do good.

For there is a lot of wasted Swearing and Scolding: and to scold is to swear.

The Evil and Good of Gossip

Once upon a time there were Two Fools. And one
of those Fools was a man and the other was a woman.
And that is a Bad Combination.

And there came unto them one of their friends, and
spake unto them, saying,

Behold, people are talking about you; and what they
say is Unpleasant. Have a care, therefore, lest what they
say become More Unpleasant.

And when the Two Fools heard this, they spake one
to another, and said,

We should worry about what People Say. For we
have done nothing amiss, and we shall do nothing amiss.
And they who speak evil of us see only the evil that
is in their own hearts. They are Idle Gossips. Let them
talk. We will give them something to Talk About.

Then these Two Fools proceeded to give the Gossips something to Talk About. And they succeeded beyond their Fondest Hopes.

And the more people talked, the more Defiant these
Two Fools became.

And when they had gotten themselves into a Pretty
Bad Mess of Publick Scandal, then did the Woman
Fool come unto Keturah, and the Man Fool came unto
me.

And we had what might be called a Foursome.

And the Woman Fool wept much; and the Man
Fool swore.

And I said unto them, Ye are Two Fools with less
than a Single Thought; two Nuts, and both of you
Cracked.

And they said, Behold, we have done no wrong. Let the evil be unto those who evil think.

And I said, Nay; the evil is also unto those who cause others to think evil.

And the man said, When a man knoweth that he hath done nothing wrong, then may he stand in his Conscious Rectitude and face the Lying, Foul-mouthed world.

And I said, Save thine eloquence. For a righteous cause a man may face the world, but not for the sake of indulging his own Folly.

And Keturah spake unto the Woman Fool, and said, My dear, this world is prone to judge that things mean what they seem to mean. Thou must not do the things that seem evil and expect the world to reckon it unto thee for good. If we are taught not to let our good be evil spoken of, much more must we not let our folly appear as if it had been evil.

And the Woman Fool said, I think that Gossip is the Vilest Thing in the World.

And I said, Gossip is indeed an unlovely thing. But it hath its Value to a Community.

And the man said, Thou speakest falsely. It hath no Value.

And I said, If it were not for the fear of Gossip, and the Wholesome Dread of what people would say, then would Fools such as ye are behave even worse than they now do; and that is a Plenty.

And I said, There are Fools that may be brayed in a Mortar with a Pestle and their folly will not depart from them. That Mortar is Public Sentiment, and that Pestle is Gossip. The braying is a Painful Process, but for you it may be Profitable.

Now it came to pass that those Two Fools were not quite Hopeless Fools. And they did as I and Keturah told them to do. And by this time their Folly is well-nigh forgotten.

The Kind of People in Our Town

There were two men who came newly into the City wherein I dwell. And it came to pass that they came both of them to visit me on the day of their arrival. For the one of them desired that he might borrow a Screwdriver: and the other besought me that he might use my Telephone to call up the Gas Company and the Electrick Light Company and the Butcher and the Baker and the Candlestick Maker.

And they inquired of me, both of them, saying,

What Kind of People live in this Town, and of what Sort of Folk are my neighbors?

And of each of them I asked, saying,

What Kind of neighbors didst thou leave behind thee; and of what Sort were the Folk in the Old Home Town?

And the first of them answered and said,

The Town I come from is an One Horse Town: and the Folk are a set of Four-Flushers; and they spend more money than they earn; and they are Unneighborly and Unpleasant; and they have so many Scandals that we kept ourselves apart like Lot in Sodom; because our righteous souls were vexed within us; and we shook off the dust of our feet and fled from that Burg and we looked not back.

And I said unto him, Thou wilt find this Town very much the same.

And while he yet Spake, the other came; and he asked of me the same question. And I likewise inquired of him concerning the Folk in his Old Home Town.

And he said,

They were fine Folk; and good neighbors; and it gave us pain to leave them; but Business called us here, and we had to leave our dear old friends.

And I said, It is the same in this Town; and thou wilt find the People just as fine and good.

And the first man heard, and he was horrified; and he said,

Verily, thou art an old Liar; for thou didst tell me the folk of this Town were a Bunch of Grafters, and a Gang of Thugs.

And I said unto them both,

Listen unto me, and consider what I say. For I have told you both the truth. There are in Every Town two sorts of Folk. There are as many kinds of Folk in this town as there be in Oshkosh or Kalamazoo or Medicine Hat or Benares or Hong Kong. Thou canst find either sort.

But what I said is still more true; for each man is likely to find the town of the same sort as himself. May the Lord deliver me from having as a Neighbor a man who cometh from a Town of which he speaketh ill. For then should the word of the Prophet be fulfilled, saying,

And I will shew no mercy, saith the Lord, but will deliver every man into the hand of his neighbor.

And I said unto them both,

If thou wouldest live in a good Town, be good thyself. So shall thine own Town be partly good, and

thou shalt be the good in it, and help to make it better.
It is a dirty bird that doth befoul its own nest, and a
mighty poor Citizen who doth knock his own Town.

The Contented Conductor

The Conductor who took up my Ticket had upon
his arm many Golden Stripes. And I said unto him,
I perceive that thou hast been long upon the Road.

And he said, Forty and two years have I been a
Passenger Conductor, and before that I ran a Freight,
and before that I was a Brakeman.

And I said, Thou dost not look it.

And he said, If I still have Vigor for a man of
mine age it is because I have learned two things. The
first is to think first what is best and endeavor to
attain it. The next is to be content with what I get.
For how shall a man do otherwise and profess to trust
his God?

Now, in about two hours the rear Truck of the
Tender of the Locomotive jumped the track. And the
Train was going fast, so that before it stopped it ran
for more than its length, and the deep cuts of the
Derailed Truck showed in the Ties behind the Train.
And it was lucky that we were not Piled in an Heap.

And I walked forward to the Locomotive and stood
beside the Conductor as he directed the Train Crew.
And he gave them few orders, but when he spake they
got busy and did as he said.

And I inquired of him, saying, Is thy Philosophy
working well?

And he answered, Sure thing. We have everything to be thankful for. No one is hurt. The Truck is uninjured. The day is fine for outdoor work. And I have a Train Crew that can coax a recalcitrant truck back on the track like Mary's Little Lamb.

And even as he spake, the Flanges returned to the Rails, and the Whistle blew for the Flagman, and the Conductor said, All Aboard.

Then did the Conductor come back and speak unto me, saying,

Thou art a Scholar. I am a Roughneck. But if I had thine Ability and thy Pulpit, then would I stand and speak unto men and women, saying,

Hearken unto me, and take good heed. Thine Imagination can depict no Heaven fairer than this Good Old World might be if ye would only take it at its best, and Trust God, and stop worrying. For which is worse, to be an Atheist and believe in no God, or to profess to believe in God and then distrust His care? Surely if there be any sin against the Holy Ghost is it not this, to profess to believe in the Guidance of God, and then to worry as if the Devil Owned the Planet and was keeping it for Home Consumption?

And I said unto him, Though thou call thyself a Roughneck, yet dost thou preach a Mighty Practical Gospel.

And he said, Yea, and I live it. Therefore have I on mine arm these many stripes, and in mine heart the song of youth and the joy of life. And it costeth very little, and the wealth of rubies is not to be compared unto it.

Now the Train had lost but Forty Minutes, which is not much more than it sometimes taketh to replace

a Punctured Tire. But the Train sped on its way, and
we pulled in On Time.

And I bowed before him as I left the Train, and
shook his hand. And he said, A quiet mind tendeth to a
level head. Therefore do we the more quickly get back
upon the Rails, with good courage, and good steam
pressure, and here we are.

And there we were, even as he said.

The Strawberry Sundae

I went unto the Shop where they sell Books; for
I desired to buy a Book. And the daughter of the
daughter of Keturah went with me. And we rode together on the Trolley Cars, and we had a good time.

And when we came to the place where they sell
Books, then did I show her a Picture Book while I
looked over the New Books. And I bought one or two.

And when we departed, she said unto me, Grandpa,
wilt thou buy for me an Ice Cream Cone?

And I said, I will surely do so; and if thou shalt
say, Please, then will I do even better.

And she said, Please.

And we came unto a place where they sell Sweets,
and we went within.

And I said, Shall I buy for thee a Sundae?

And she said, I have never eaten a Sundae, but I
should like it very much.

And I said, What flavor wilt thou have?

And she said, I desire Chocolate.

So I bought for her a Chocolate Sundae, but as for myself, I bought Strawberry. For I think the Strawberry is the next to the best Berry that the Lord ever made (the best being the Red Raspberry, which I like much).

So the little maiden ate her Chocolate Sundae, and liked it exceeding well. But she liked the Ripe, Rich, Red, Juicy Color of my Strawberry. So that she looked over now and then and almost wished that she had not ordered Chocolate. And when I saw that she was Interested, I ate slowly, so that when she had finished, I had only begun. And that was Rather Hard upon the little maiden.

Now, when she had finished, she clasped her little hands together, and she leaned her little round elbows on the table, and she rested her chin on her little clasped hands, and she looked over at my dish, and she said:

It looks so nice that I will not ask for any.

Now, when I heard that, I did smile. For I thought it the very prettiest way of asking for a thing I had ever heard.

And I thought of the people whose only way of asking God for things is to tease Him, and say, Give me this, and be quick about it for Christ's sake.

For I wonder how any man doth dare to say for Christ's sake when he is asking something for his own sake, and whether it doth not sound unto the angels like swearing.

For of all the sins which good Christian men commit, it seemeth to me that among the gravest may be the undisguised selfishness of their prayers.

And I wondered how to teach Christian men and women to ask for things as prettily as the daughter of the daughter of Keturah asked for the Strawberry Sundae.

For I might just mention in closing that she got all the Strawberry Sundae she desired when she asked for it in that way.

The Traffic Cop and the Blind Man

I walked in the streets of a City, which was for greatness like unto Nineveh or Babylon. And I came unto a place where two ways met. And the traffic was something fierce. And there stood in the middle of the street that ran north and south, and also in the middle of the street that ran east and west, a Guardian of the Public Welfare. And he was great of girth, and tall like Goliath of Gath. And he wore a Blue Coat with Brass Buttons. And on his hands were White Gloves, symbolic of the purity of the Municipal Government.

And he blew an Whistle one time. And all the east and west traffic stopped, and it piled up on both sides of the street as the Waters of the Red Sea rose up when Moses, the servant of God, stretched forth his hand upon them. But all the north and south traffic moved on.

Then did he blow his Whistle twice. And all the east and west traffic flowed through, while the north and south traffic stood in an heap like the waters of Jordan in the days of Joshua, the son of Nun. And the people who were going east and west went over dry-shod and in safety.

And presently all traffic stopped both ways, for the Whistle blew not, but the Traffic Cop raised his right hand. And all the Teamsters and the Chauffeurs and the Mahouts and even some of the Women Shoppers stood and obeyed his Gesture.

And the Traffic Cop left his place in the middle of the intersection of the Two Streets, and walked across the street unto the Curb. And I looked, and behold, a Blind Man. And he was Confused.

And the Policeman took him by the arm, and led him over. Neither did he say unto him, Step lively, please. But he led the Blind Man to the Opposite Curb, and made a way for him among the Women Shoppers, so that they stood back and let him through.

Then did the Traffic Cop return unto his place and blow his Whistle, and the tides of Commerce and of Humanity flowed on.

And there was not a Chauffeur who saw it who swore at the Cop, neither was there any who beheld it who reproved him. For they had been impatient of every other delay, but they willingly waited while he led a Blind Man to safety.

And I thought of the Immutable Decrees of God, and of the Laws whereby He doth govern the Universe, how they are as right as the One Whistle for the north and south traffic and the Two Whistles for the east and west traffic. But I had a suspicion, which in me is a mighty faith, that without violating any of His Immutable Laws, the Great God can somehow care for His own. Yea, I have lived long, and I have sometimes seen

the evidence that God leadeth the blind by a way that
he knoweth not, but in a right way, and a way that
is better than he could choose for himself.

For the Apostle Paul hath said that the Policeman
is a Minister of God, and I know not why one should
not learn from him a sermon.

Things Not to Be Forgotten

I rode upon a Railway Train, Somewhere in Kansas,
and the Train stopped Thirty Minutes for Lunch.
And at one end of the Station was there a little Park,
with two great Sun Dials, whereof one showed Central
Time and the other showed Mountain Time. And the
Park was attractive, and had Cost the Railway Some
Coin, and the result was worth it.

Now there stood in the little Park, hard by the
Train, a strong White Post, as it were two cubits in
height. And there was framed in the top of the post an
old-time Drawbar, with a Coupling-Pin and a Link.
And upon the Post was painted in Black Letters this
superscription, Lest We Forget.

And I said unto myself, It may be that this is the
town where the man lived who first invented the Safety
Coupler.

And I entered the Station, and I inquired of the
Young Man who was Clerk of the Station Hotel. And
I asked of him, saying,

Wherefore is that Post with the old Drawbar erected
in this Town rather than in another?

And he said, Where is it at? For I have never seen it.

And I inquired of another, and he said,

Thou mayest search me; for I have never noticed it.

And I inquired of the Station Agent, and he said, I once knew, but, behold, I have forgotten.

Then did the Conductor say, All Aboard, and I got on board.

And I considered the days of my boyhood, when I played about the Cars, and I knew Railway men; and many of them had lost fingers that were crushed in coupling cars; and many lost their hands, and others lost their lives.

And I said, Behold, there was a man who considered all these things, and sat up nights, and peradventure pawned his Shirt that he might invent a method of avoiding all this. And here is his memorial, marked, Lest We Forget; and some men pass it every day and never see it; and others once knew its meaning but they have forgotten.

And I looked out of the car window, and I beheld a Church, and upon the Church was a Spire, and upon the Spire was a Cross.

And I thought of the multitudes who continually pass it by, and I was grieved in mine heart; for I said, Among them are those who say, I have never seen it; and others say, I have seen it, but what it meaneth, behold, I know not. And others say, Behold, I once knew, but I have forgotten.

The Car Wheels

A certain man labored in the Division Terminal of a great Railway. And it was so that when a Train entered the Station, that there they changed Engines, and Train-crews. And certain men put Ice in the Coolers, and Water in the Tanks. And there were times when certain others swabbed the Windows so that they might be seen through; but this did not always occur. And the duty which was assigned unto this man was this, that he should begin at the head of the Train, and walk the length of it, and stoop down and strike every Car Wheel with an Hammer. And he did Precisely as he was told. For he walked the length of every train, and struck every wheel on the right side thereof, and then turned himself about and walked back upon the other side of the Train and the wheels upon that side did he strike in like manner. And this he did quickly, so that he had it done by the time other men had put Ice in the Coolers and Waste and Dope in the Boxes of the Axles, and the Engines had been changed.

Now it came to pass that after many years the General Superintendent spake unto the President of the Road, and he said, Behold, this man hath been on our Pay-roll for Five and Twenty years, and he hath never missed a day. Let us Celebrate, and Recognize his Faithfulness, and give him a Gold Watch, and a Pass for himself and his Wife unto California and back, and a little purse of Gold which he may blow in on a good time. And they did even so.

And while the celebration was in progress someone asked of him, saying,

What is the reason why the wheels must be struck? And what is the occasion thereof?

And he said, Thou mayest search me. I know nothing save that I draw my pay for hitting the wheels, and I hit them every time and never miss a wheel.

But he had never listened to the ring of the hammer that he might hear whether the wheels were sound or cracked, neither had he known nor regarded. But he had done his job and drawn his pay for twenty-five years.

Now when I heard this tale, I said, That man is not so infrequent as some might suppose. There are many who go through life in like manner. They do the day's job and draw their pay and never think what it all is for. Yea, there might even be such men in the pulpit, but may God forbid; and there are such in many another vocation.

And I prayed my God for all men, that they may labor, not only to strike the wheels but to listen for the ring.

For there are those who strike the wheels and go on, and if the Train run through, they say it is the result of Careful Supervision, and if the wheel crack, and the train land in the Ditch, they say it is a Mysterious Providence.

And there are such men, not a few, who obtain their living by labor no more intelligent than this, and some of them less continuous. And some of them travel on passes and receive the praise of men.

But God knoweth whether men listen for the ring, or whether they only hit the wheels.

The Minister and the Saw

Now there came to me one of the sons of the Prophets, even a young minister, and he said, My Church treateth me harshly.

And I said, What hast thou done to thy Church?

And he said, I upbraided them, and I told them they were Miserable Sinners.

And I answered, Thou didst speak truthfully and unwisely.

And he said, Is it not wise to speak the truth?

And I said, It is not wise to speak anything else; but Truth is precious, and should be used with Economy.

And he said, There were Great Reforms that needed to be wrought in that Town, and a Great Work to be done, and I had hoped to Inspire the Church to Do Those Things. But they are Stiff-necked, and they seek to Fire me.

And I said to him, Come with me into my Garden.

And we went out into the Garden, and I took with me a Saw.

And I said, Climb thou this tree, for thou art younger than I.

And he climbed the Tree, and sat upon a limb thereof as I showed him.

And I said, That limb needeth to be Cut Off. Take thou the saw and Cut it Off.

And he began to saw beyond him.

And I said, Saw on the other side.

And he began to saw, but he stopped, and he said, If I saw the limb between myself and the Tree, I shall surely fall.

And I said unto him, The minister who pusheth a Reform faster than his Church will follow him, and findeth himself Fired, is like unto the man who Ascendeth a Tree, and Saweth off a Limb between himself and the Tree.

And I left him there, and I went into mine House. And he sat there Some Little Time in Deep Meditation.

And he Climbed Down, and returned to his own Church. And he called the elders thereof together, and he said, I have been foolish, and have sought to Bring in the Millennium Before Sundown. Be patient with me, and I will strive to be more patient with the Church.

And they answered and said, Now thou art Talking like a man of Sense. Continue thou to chasten us for our sins, and show us how to be better, but expect not the Impossible, and lo, we will stand by thee till the Cows Come Home.

And the minister whom the Church was about to Fire took thought, and added a Cubit to his Stature; and his Church Rallied about him, and the last I heard some of the things he wanted to Get Done were being done.

And he wrote me a letter, saying,

O Safed, thou didst have me Up a Tree, but behold I am down and on the Job, and if thou wouldst see a happy and united and hustling Church, where the people love their minister, and the minister loveth his people, and where everything is up and moving, and good is being done, come over and see us.

And I read the letter and rejoiced. For there are Ministers who have learned How to Saw, but neither

When nor Where. And if they will Climb my Apple
Tree I will teach them wisdom.

The Value of Things Despised

Now there is an Handmaiden of the Lord whom
I know and Honor, and she had an Accident, so that
her Arm was Bound Up in a Sling. And I went to see
her that I might Comfort her in her Affliction.

And I found her very Cheerful, for such is her
Wont.

And I asked her what ailed her Arm, and she
answered that she thought it was a Sprain, but that
the Physician had given it a name such as Physicians
give unto the ills of people who can afford it. And he
told her that it would be well in a Fortnight or There-
about, but meantime to be Careful, and look well to
her Diet, and have a Specialist examine her Tonsils
and have an X-Ray made of her Teeth. For such is the
habit of Physicians.

And I said, I am glad that it will soon be well.
Meantime, be thou thankful that it is thy Left Hand.

And she answered and said, O Safed, art thou a
Wise man, and hast thou nothing better to say to
me? Behold, I have learned a better lesson than that.

And I asked her, What is the Lesson?

And she said, I am finding every blessed minute
of the day how few things I can do with my Right
Hand alone. Wherefore, I am thanking God that all
these years I have had a good Left Hand, as well as
a Right.

And I meditated, and I said, Thou hast well said. Well would it be for us all if we could learn thus the value of the things we despise. For the Right Hand is from God, and so also is the Left; and he who loveth his Right Hand should not forget to thank God that He hath given him the Left Hand also.

The Flesh and the Spirit

There came unto me one of the Sons of the Prophets; and he was a goodly young man. His Brow was High and Pale, and so was the rest of him. And he took himself Seriously, which is not a Bad Thing to do if one work not overtime on the job.

And forasmuch as Keturah had other fish to fry on that day, I took him to Luncheon at a Restaurant.

And he looked upon the bill of fare and heaved a sigh. And he said, I have to be Very Careful of my Eating.

And he spake unto the Waitress, and he said, Give me a Very Thin Slice of Toast, and a Very Soft Boiled Egg, and a Cup of Hot Water.

Now I thought that it would do him good to receive a Little Jolt.

And I spake unto the Waitress, and I said, Bring unto me a Thick, Juicy Beefsteak, and a Baked Potato with a Trap Door in the Top, and a Chunk of Butter in the Trap Door, and some Paprika sprinkled round about the Butter; and bring unto me also a Cup of Coffee, and a Quarter Section of Hot Mince Pie with the Bark On, and a Slice of Cheese with the Pie.

And the Waitress smiled a Little Subjective Smile, for she knew that I did not always go in quite so Heavy, and she surmised that it was an Object Lesson. But she spake nothing, save that she said, Yessir. And she departed.

And the young man was Astonished.

And he said, Thou art a man with Gray Hair, yet dost thou give thought to what thou shalt eat and drink.

And I said, That is just where thou dost fool thyself. It is thou who givest thought to it. For thou dost ever consider what thou shalt eat and what thou must not eat; whereas I think not of it at all; but when I come to the Table, then do I eat, and give God thanks that I have food and good digestion.

And he said, With such an Appetite, I wonder thou art not dead long since.

And I said, Thou wilt be dead before thou art half my age if thou forget not to think about thy Digestion.

And I said unto him, My son, hearken unto me, and learn wisdom. It is not for nothing that the Good God hath put our Stomach and all the Organs thereunto appertaining out of our sight. It is not the overloading of the stomach that killeth men so much as the overloading of the mind. I am this day eating more than is my wont; but I shall get away with it, and thou wilt have Nervous Indigestion over thy Nursing Bottle Stuff.

And I said unto him, Rise early in the morning. Get a little exercise before Breakfast. Eat lightly but sufficiently, and get in a good morning's work. Get out in the afternoon, and make thy Parish Calls on foot, and make about five times as many of them as thou art now making. Then shalt thou come to the table with such appetite that thou couldst eat an Horse with the Harness on. Eat heartily, yet not as a Glutton. Leave the table while thou art still Capable but not Desirous. As for the kind of food which thou devourest, eat what is set before thee and ask no questions, save it be for a second helping. It is not that which goeth into a man which causeth indigestion, but the evil thoughts of whether it is safe for him to eat this or that or so much. The man who preacheth hath need of a good flow of Red Blood. For him a Beefsteak is a means of Grace. And when thou hast eaten and art full, give thanks to God; and as for thy Digestion, Forget It.

Now in after days he came again to me, and he said, To see a man of thine age consume a Beefsteak and a Hot Mince Pie was to me of more worth than half that I learned in the School of the Prophets.

And I beheld that he was no longer Pale, but a sure enough Man.

The Hornets' Nest

When Summer cometh, I and Keturah we leave the City behind us, and we go Far From the Madding Crowd to a place where there are Trees and a Little Lake. And the trees of the Lord are full of sap, and also full of Birds and Squirrels and such like things. And we suffer no man to harm them; yea, our children spent their summers there, and played among them and made friends of them and harmed them not.

Now when we arrived at the beginning of this

summer, behold, there was a great Nest of Hornets in one of the trees hard by the house. And it was certain days before we saw it.

Then came to us certain who said, Destroy it, for it will make thee trouble.

And they said, Know ye that these are no Nice Little Yellow Jackets with a Gentle Sting; for these be the Regular Old-Fashioned Big Black Fellows, with a sting about an Inch Long; and the way they sting is Something Fierce; and when one of them cometh after a fellow, then do they all come, and settle upon him so that he is Black with them, and sting him mightily.

And I said, Those hornets saw us several days before we saw them, and they troubled us not. So long as they behave like Gentlemen or Ladies or whichever they ought to be, I will harm them not.

So we let them alone.

And I and Keturah we watched them as they went in and out of the many holes of their Nest. For the Nest was larger than the head of a man. And they worked so that compared to them the Little Busy Bee is a Sluggard. And they paid no manner of attention to us. Yea, we came near and beheld, and they went on about their business.

And I considered how foolish it had been to try to destroy the Nest; for then had they stung us; yea, and those that escaped had remained and come at us daily until either we or they were driven out.

But the good God hath given unto them some measure of the joy of life, and they menace us not save as we trouble them.

Wherefore did we mind our own business, and the

hornets did the same. Neither did we in all the summer get one sting, or have one hornet fly at us.

And I considered how many men there are who continually Hunt Trouble. For whenever they see any sort of thing that doth irritate them, then do they throw a club at it and get stung good and plenty. And then do they come with a pole and a rag soaked in coal oil and get stung some more. And so it goeth with them all through life. Whereas there is a More Excellent Way.

For both I and the Hornets we minded our own business. And the Hornets are still there. And no man molesteth them or maketh them afraid.

This parable teacheth that it is well for a man that he mind his own business.

Good Health and Veracity

I met a man, and I saluted him and said, Good Morning.

And he answered me with a Grunt.

And I said unto him, It is a Fine Day.

And he said, It may be, but I feel Sick.

And I said, According as thou feelest, so art thou.

And he said, A fellow cannot help feeling bad when he doth feel bad.

And I said, Thou art most surely wrong. Where dost thou feel ill?

And he said, I was out late last night at a Party, and I went to bed Two Whole Hours later than usual,

and I slept but an Half Hour later than I commonly
do, and I rushed for my train. Therefore doth my Head
Ache and I feel ill.

And I said unto him, How many arms hast thou, and
do they ache?

And he said, They are all right and their number is
Two.

And I said, How many fingers hast thou on each
hand, that would pain thee if any one of them were
cut or broken?

And he said, I have ten fingers, but I see not what
that has to do with it.

I said unto him, Take heed to what I say and learn
wisdom. The two hours of sleep that thou didst lose
are something, but not much. It is thine extra half hour
in bed that aileth thee. Thou shouldest have risen a
little earlier than usual and burned a little more Oxygen.
If thine head felt Rocky, thou shouldest have said,
I have two good Legs, which are all right, and I will
stretch them with a little walk. I have two good Arms,
and I will swing them. I have two good Eyes and I
will fill them with the Beauty of the Morning. I have
two good Lungs, and they pain me not; I will cram
them with Fresh Air. I have two good Ears, and never
an Earache; I will listen to the Birds as I walk.

And I said unto him, I am accustomed to going
to bed two hours later than usual. It is not the loss of
sleep that hurteth a man if he lose a little more in
getting fresh air.

And he said, Thou speakest words of folly. If a man
lose sleep, he must make it up; and if he feeleth ill,
there is no reason why he should lie about it.

And I said, According as a man thinketh in his heart so is he well or ill. The good God who made this world hath put into it that wherewith we may be strong, and he who riseth in the morning with a heavy feeling in his head ought to have more sense than to lie later than usual and gorge his breakfast and run for the train, and then blaspheme his God by telling the world that he feeleth ill.

And he said, It is just possible that thou speakest a little bit of good sense, and I have not considered it before.

And I said unto him, Consider it now, and it shall be worth more than an whole Apothecary Shop to thee.

Failure and Success

Keturah made a Cake. And the manner of making it was this. She baked it in Three Sections, and when they came from the Oven, she laid them one upon another so that the Cake was Three Stories in Height. And between the layers she placed Frosting, yea, and more Frosting upon the top thereof. And into the Frosting did she put handfuls of meat out of the Cocoanut. For there be many kinds of cake that I like, even every kind that Keturah doth make, but the best of all is the kind that is made with Cocoanut.

And when she served the Cake, she said, Alas, my lord, it is a Failure.

And I said, Wherefore should it be a Failure?

And she answered, The Telephone did ring just

when the Frosting should have been attended to, and it hath not sufficiently hardened. Yea, it is Sticky, and a Failure.

And when I beheld it, lo, very much of the Frosting had run down the sides of the Cake. Nevertheless, there was much of it still upon the top, and between the layers, and the Cocoanut was all to the Good.

And I said, Since it is a Failure, it were well to eat more of it, and put the Poor Thing out of Sight.

And Keturah said, Thou hast well said. Eat thou another slice, and yet another.

And I did as I was bidden. And albeit the Cake was a trifle Sticky, there was nothing else that was not one hundred percent to the good.

Therefore, when she maketh something that is Unusually Good, I say unto her, Is not this a Failure? For I desire another piece.

And I would that we might somehow readjust life that all life's Failures might somehow make for success. Yea, I remember that my God hath promised that in some way that I know not the wrath of man shall praise Him.

For if this world, which is a cake not turned, can scrape some of the char from its overdone side, and bake the side that is dough so that it can be eaten, then shall I rejoice. For I would believe that this world is a success, and by faith I so accept it.

The Unidentified Taste

I was once a Lad, and I loved Candy. And the Candy of that day came not in Boxes at a Dollar and the Half of a Dollar for a Pound, else had I never seen any of it with a Telescope. But it came in Sticks. And the price of a Stick of Candy was a Cent. And if one had great wealth, then might he obtain six sticks for Five Cents. But I seldom had Six Sticks.

Now there came unto our house a Visitor who brought unto us a small Paper Bag of Candy of another Sort. And it was of many sorts. And I ate one of the lumps, and it was more delicious than anything that I had ever eaten, or have eaten since.

It was not hard, but was more nearly soft; yet it was not utterly soft and squashy; but it had in it shreds of a substance with a flavor of its own, and it grated upon the teeth with a most celestial sensation. It gave unto the sense of taste a New Experience as of something that might have been contained in a Story Book, but never known in Real Life. It left in my mouth a Reminiscent Longing, mingled with a Happy Consciousness that I had experienced something finer of its kind than ever before had occurred to me.

Now as the years went by, and as I came to know more about the various Kinds of Candy, I bought many kinds. For I love Chocolate Creams, and Cream Patties, and Divinity Fudge and divers other kinds, and I think that I shall always care for it. And I sought for many years for a kind of Candy that should taste as did that piece which I ate in my boyhood, but I found it not.

And it hath sometimes occurred to me that it may have been Cocoanut Bar that I ate, and knew not the name of it. But I have eaten much Cocoanut Bar and it is good, but it tasted not as that tasted.

So it seemeth that I shall go through life desiring that I may once again taste something as good as that which I once tasted, and that I shall not taste it again.

For, if it be so that what I ate was Cocoanut Bar, and I have eaten other since as good, then do I surely know that it was something in me that hath been lost, and not anything in the Candy. For I can never bring to it the appetite of a Boy, though mine is a Close Approach unto it.

And I considered the men who scold their wives because they cannot cook as those men's mothers did. And I consider that their wives are better cooks than their mothers, but that the men of jaded appetites bring no longer to the table the hunger of a boy, that is able to transform very ordinary cooking into something marvelously good. And I advise those men not to demand of their wives such cooking as mother produced until they saw wood long enough to get an appetite such as mother's darling little boy was used to possess.

But if there be any good woman who maketh Home-Made Candy, and who can make me some that shall taste like that which I ate in that day when I was a boy, I would saw wood for some time for the joy of having that taste again in my mouth.

But if I never have it again, then shall no man take away from me that, or any joy that I once have had. For those joys are mine own forever.

The Worm in the Concrete Gutter

There came an Heavy Rain, so that the Angle Worms did come out of their Holes in the Earth. And one of them wriggled over the Curb into the Street, and came into the Gutter. Now that street was Macadamized, and the Curb and the Gutter were of Concrete. And the Worm Wriggled along, and he was unable to Bore an Hole through the Concrete that he might find him an home in the earth; neither could he climb again up the side of the Curb. And he was much Discouraged.

And I found him there.

And I said, This world is the world of a Good God, and in it every form of life hath some mission. I have read in a Learned Book how the Earth Worms like unto this one or its Ancestors did make this earth Fertile; else there had been no soil for the growth of such things as men do eat. And Worms are good also to feed the Early Bird, and to bait an Hook wherewith to draw out Leviathan. But where in all the providence of God is there moral meaning in the catastrophe of a Worm in a Concrete Gutter?

And I said, Little Worm, I have no present call to go a-fishing, and there is no early bird in sight. I might make an Hymn of thee, as certain men have done who call themselves Worthless Worms; but a man for whom Christ died hath no right to call himself a Worm; therefore will I cut out the Hymn Stunt, and call myself by a name either better or worse. But I have been in case like thee, where the Heavens were Brass, and the earth offered no refuge, and I should have been in Despair but for the Help of a Friend or the Love of God. Behold, I will be unto thee as God; for I have the power of life or death of thee.

And I picked up the Worm, and lifted him over the curb, and laid him on the Wet Earth.

And neither he nor the Early Bird knew that I had done this.

Even so hath God holpen me in times when I wot not of it.

Philosophy and Money

There came to me a Rich Man, who spake unto me, saying, What is a Philosopher?

And I said, As is his name, so is he; one that loveth Wisdom.

And he said, Art thou a Philosopher?

And I said, Humblest am I among the most humble of her servants; yet am I a lover of Wisdom.

And he said, I am no Philosopher, but I am a Rich Man. What dost thou consider a Rich Man to be?

And I answered, As one whom God hath blessed so richly with abundance of Soup whereon he filleth himself so that he hath no room nor appetite for the Ice Cream, so is many a Rich Man; but also there are Others. Of which sort art thou?

And he said, If thou art a Philosopher, thou shouldest know. But art not thou thyself a lover of Money? Yea, doth not every Philosopher love Money more than any Rich Man loveth Philosophy?

And I said, That question hath been asked of old. And there was a Rich Man in Olden Time who thus asked a Philosopher wiser than I. And that Philosopher answered, The reason that Philosophers care more for Money than Rich Men care for Wisdom is that Philosophers know what they Lack, and Rich Men know not.

And he said, The Philosopher who said that was a Wise Old Boy.

And I said, O thou Rich Man, thou art not altogether hopeless. Even like unto the Big Monsters of the Deep that yet are Mammals and not Fish, so hast thou something besides Gills; yea, thou hast Lungs that are fitted for More Oxygen than thou canst extract from the Salt Water of Business; and now and then must thou Come Up to Breathe.

And I said unto him,

Hearken thou to me. The Philosopher is not saved by his Philosophy, and it is Right Possible for him to be at one and the same time a Philosopher and a Fool; neither is there any way under Heaven whereby either may be saved if he use not the gift of God for the welfare of others.

And he said, Thou art indeed a Wise Old Boy.

The Autumn Hollyhocks

There came unto me a woman, being unmarried, even one whom the profane call an Old Maid, being one of those women whom the Lord loveth too well to give her unto any one man.

And she sat before me in bitterness of spirit. And she said:

I desire to open unto thee mine heart, for it is full of bitterness. There is no one on earth to whom I am necessary. Behold, thine handmaiden was once young and fair, and when young men saw me, then did they desire me. And I might have been married and the mother of children. But my parents kept me close so that young men feared to look at me. And my brothers sought wives, and married and begat sons and daughters, and sent for me to take care of their children, but I had none of mine own. Yea, and when my father and my mother grew old, then did I remain with them, and care for them, and humor them when they grew Childish. And now they are dead and buried, and their souls are in Heaven, and my life work is done. And I am an Old Maid, and life hath nothing left for me.

And she said, If I go unto a Wedding, then do men whom I have known long, and who were young when I was young, joke with me, and say, It will be thy turn next. And I smile, though I fain would murder them. For being an Old Maid is no joke when one hath done her life work and hath more years to live and nothing to live for.

And I said unto her, The sun is bright, and the day is warm, for this is the season called Indian Summer; and for this and the Moccasin and the Canoe, I do thank the American Indian. Step out with me into the Garden, for I have somewhat to show thee.

Now the Garden was laid waste by the frost, and the beauty that had been was but a memory. But at one side is there a Mulberry Tree, and beyond it a Garage where I keep old books, and an Hoe and a Shovel and an Wheelbarrow; for I have no Automobile save an Wheelbarrow and the Cars of my friends, who are Many.

And under the shade of the Mulberry Tree, hard by the Garage, was there an Hollyhock in Full Bloom. And the color thereof was beautiful.

And she exclaimed concerning it, and wondered with great admiration that it was so late in Bloom, and the Blossoms so beautiful.

And I said unto this woman, even unto this Unappropriated Blessing who is called an Old Maid,

Thou art like unto this Hollyhock.

And she said, Do not mock thine handmaiden.

And I said, This Hollyhock was shaded by the Mulberry Tree and by the Garage, so that it grew slowly. But when the heat of the Summer fell upon the Garden, then did this Hollyhock grow secure and wilt not. And now when Frosts have fallen upon other Flowers, it blossometh like the Spring.

And I said unto her, Put on thy prettiest frock, and tire thine hair becomingly, and drop ten years from thine age, and go forth and blossom. For God hath yet work for thee even though thou live single. Yea, and because men are very Susceptible Creatures, who knoweth whether there be some Perfectly Good Widower looking for just such a Late-Blooming Flower as thou shalt be? And if not, still is it better to Blossom than to die with frost at the heart.

And the next time I beheld her, she looked ten years younger; and certain men did sit up and take notice.

And I counted this among my Good Deeds.

The Little Girl in the Blue Dress

I rode upon a Train from New York even unto Chicago. And the Train was Full. And among the rest was there a Young Mother with a Little Girl. And they were going unto South Bend and the little damsel wore a Blue Dress.

And the little maiden and I became friends; for Little Girls like me, and I do verily believe that Good Little Girls are made of Sugar and Spice and all that is Nice.

And she had Dominoes wherewith to play. And she sat with me, and we set up the Dominoes to make Beds. And we made of them Single Beds, and Double Beds, and we tried to make Beds such as were in the Train, but we did not succeed very well.

And we had ridden all night and much of the day, and it drew toward evening. And I said, This place is Elkhart, and the miles unto Chicago are an Hundred and One; and here do they cut off the Dining Car, and it is our last long stop. And we shall reach Chicago in Two Hours and Twenty Minutes, and South Bend will be before that.

And she said, I would that South Bend were farther.

And I inquired of her why she said so.

And she said, There will be Very Hard Letters to learn in South Bend.

And I said, Why dost thou think there will be Hard Letters to learn?

And she said, I had just begun to go to school when my father got a new job in South Bend and sent for us. And I learned A and B and C all the way down to X and Y and Z, and how to spell CAT and DOG and COW and many more. And my mother says that now I must begin all over again. And the Letters will be different; and who knoweth how they spell COW in South Bend?

And I said, Fear not. They spell it mostly with a C, and only a few of them begin it with a K.

And she said, It will all be so different, and I fear it. I wish this old Train would go on and on, and never come to South Bend.

And I saw that the little maiden was sore distressed by reason of the Very Hard Letters.

And I said unto her, Fear not, my dear. I have been in South Bend; yea, I have passed through it an hundred times. The letters there are A and B and C, and X and Y and Z, and there are twenty-six of them and no more.

And she inquired, Art thou sure?

And I said, Sure thing. And CAT and DOG are the same as in New York, and all that thou didst learn there will be good in South Bend.

And the little maiden was comforted.

Now this hooting, whanging train of human life moveth swiftly; and ever and anon there getteth on some passenger who wondereth how it will be in the place to which he journeyeth, and who approacheth life's destination with fear. And I prayed unto my God that He would send unto all such some of His Experienced Angels, who would say to all such timid souls, Fear not. The Alphabet of Heaven is the kindly deeds and gracious words which thou hast learned in the Kindergarten of Life. Heaven and Earth have a Common Alphabet, and all that thou hast learned will be of value there.

And the little maiden flung a kiss toward me as the Train pulled out of South Bend, and I beheld her in the arms of her father.

Seeing the Fire Engine

My little Grandson came unto my house, and he was Sobbing.

And I inquired, saying, Why is my little lad grieved?

And he burst into piteous Lamentation, and he cried, I want to see the Fire Engine.

And his mother spake, saying, We came past the Engine House, and the Firemen were Washing the Engine. And he desired to tarry, but I said, We will stop as we return from the Post-office. And behold, when we returned, the Firemen had taken the Engine inside, so that we saw it no more.

There are sorrows great and sorrows small; but the sorrow of the small boy who hath desired to see the

Fire Engine and hath not seen it is the Sorrow of Calamity.

And the little lad cried sore, saying, I want to see the Fire Engine.

And I said, Come with me, for we shall surely see the Fire Engine.

And as we started there came a man to see me, but I said, Tarry thou till I return, or come again another day, for I am busy.

And we went unto the Engine House. And I spake unto the Chief, and I saluted him, and he saluted me. And I said, We desire to see the Fire Engine.

And the Chief took the little lad and set him on high, so that he sat far up on the seat behind the Steering Wheel. And the Chief gave him the Bell Rope, and the little lad pulled the rope so that the Bell Rang.

And he saw the Ladders and the Truck, and the Chemical Engine, and the Whole Business.

And certain of the Firemen ascended the stairs, and slid down the Brass Pole that he might see how they descended when there was a Fire.

And the little lad had the Time of his Life.

Moreover, I had a Pretty Tolerably Good Time myself. For I am not too old to remember when I chased the Fire Engine.

So the little lad and I we came again, and I left him with Keturah, and with his mother the daughter of Keturah. And they said, Have you two Small Boys seen the Fire Engine?

And we answered and said, We have seen it. And my Grandson told about the High Seat and the Bell and the Brass Pole and the Chief.

Now it came to pass that night when I said my

Prayers, that I spake unto Keturah, saying, Some good
things have I done this day, and some it may be not
so good. But one mighty good deed have I done: I
let my work Go Hang for an hour while I went with
the lad to see the Fire Engine.

For he who doeth a kind deed unto a little child,
doeth it for all the long years that lie ahead of that
young life. Wherefore do I say unto all men, Skimp
not thy deeds of kindness to any sort of man or
woman, but the good deed that lasteth longest is that
which thou shalt do unto a little child.

And moreover, it is an Whole Lot of Fun.

The Wives of the Prophet

I and Keturah we were invited to a Reception.
And Keturah inquired of me, saying, Which dress shall
I wear? Shall it be my New one or my Blue one or the
One I wore Last?

And I said, Let it be the Blue one.

And she said, I will wear All Three.

For this is our Little Joke; and her New Blue Last-
Worn Dress looketh good unto me when Keturah hath
it on.

And I said, There will be no woman there so fair
as thou. For her Cheeks were red, and she stepped
off as if she were Sixteen.

And she said, O my lord, there is nothing more
pleasing unto a woman than to look well in the eyes of
the man whom she doth love. Nevertheless, I cannot

forget the years or the gray hair which the years have brought. God grant I may always look well in thine eyes.

And I said, Sure thing.

And I said, There was once a Prophet named Mohammed; and there are those who think that he was a False Prophet, but that concerneth not my story. And he had a wife whose name was Kadijah. And it came to pass after long years that she died. And he despaired of filling her place with any one woman, and he married many wives. And one of them was his Favorite, and her name was Ayesha.

And it came to pass that Ayesha inquired of Mohammed, saying, Am I not very beautiful? And he said, Yea.

And she inquired, Dost thou not love me? And he answered, Yea.

And she said, Am not I thy Favorite? And Mohammed looked around to be sure that none of his other wives were listening in, and he answered, Yea.

And she inquired yet further, Dost thou not love me more than thou lovest any of thine other wives?

And again he looked around, and he answered softly, Yea.

And if Ayesha had been wise she would have stopped there. But there was one question which she wanted to ask more than all, and she made the mistake of asking it.

And she said, O Mohammed, thou great and noble man, dost thou not love me more than thou didst love Kadijah? For she grew old and had wrinkles and gray hair, and I am young and fair.

And Mohammed answered with a Great Oath, and he said,

Nay, by Allah! For she it was who first believed in me!

And I said unto Keturah, Though all the fair women in the world were placed in line, and I were led admiring down the length of it, yet would I find no one among them all who could create for me the memories of our struggles and anxieties and economies and our meager triumphs and our sweet and holy joys. Thou in thy New Blue Last-Worn Dress art unto thy husband the fairest among women.

And Keturah said nothing, but she found my hand as we walked away together, and she gave it a little squeeze.